W9-AYE-937

OLD MAN WINTER

& other sordid tales

by J.T. Yost

The old man is always cold.

3
FLOOR
hrf
huff
hrrfff

183
MOOSE!!
CH-CHK
Ch

ICED COFFEE
DOUBLE BREWED, ENJOYED REPEATEDLY.

SUBWAY

COSTILLA

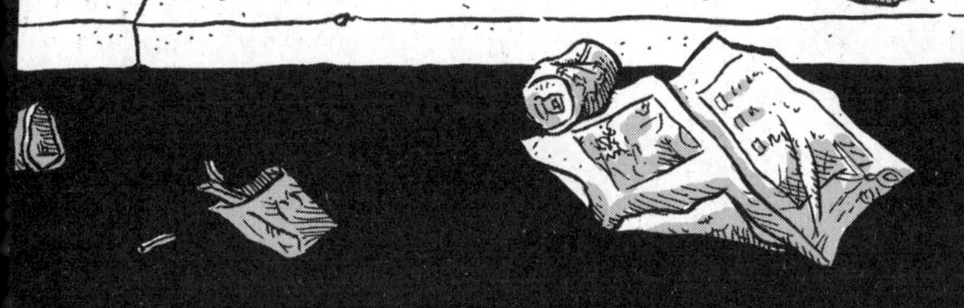

1:30

It's worse at night. He always wakes up shivering, even with three blankets.

Hello there, young fellers!

Hello there, young fellers!

u-Save
Art Supplies
Winter SALE
SALE!
Ching ching
Art Supplies

....and I would always tell her, "Don't eat the seeds. **Never** eat the seeds. They're **bad** for you!

But she'd do it anyway. Probably just to see what I would do!

Yeah, I don't eat the seeds.

Okay, that's good. That's good.

Well, I guess I'll see you on Tuesday, right?

Yep, yep. Take care...

Don't let me catch you eating the seeds!

ha ha!
ACRYLIC
GOLDEN ACRYLIC

Ching
Ching
Sorry! We're
CLOSED
AIDS
WALK
GESSO

He's a nice enough guy.

It kind of creeps me out how he always brings up his wife, though.

I assume she must be dead 'cause he always refers to her in the **past tense**.
AIDS WALK

Yeah, that **is** creepy.

I can help you over at this register, ma'am...

185
183
Hey Dad. Buzz me in!

So, how ya doin', pop?
Oh, you know me... great! Great!

Yeah?

You seemed kind of distant on the phone...

Naaaah... I was just **tired** is all.

crinkle
crin

I was thinking I'd come by later this week to help you get rid of some stuff before you move...
Maybe we could have a stoop sale or something!
Oh, I don't have too much to get rid of...
I'll just take it to the Salvation Army.

re you kidding me?

You can't take all this junk with you!! Most of it was MOM'S anyhow!!

Surely you don't need a closetful of women's clothing.

...or this ashtray.

You don't even smoke!

Dad, c'mon... You were always telling her what a filthy habit smoking is...

Don't tell me **you've** taken it up!

crinkle
crinkl

Okay, that's what I thought.

We're getting rid of all this, alright?
it's depressing.

Want some more coffee?

Winter
SALE
OPEN

Oh! I talked to my friend and she says you probably have bad circulation.

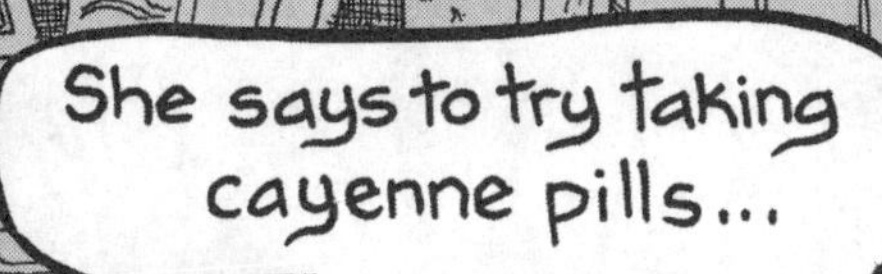
She says to try taking cayenne pills...
Supposed to be good for the circulation.

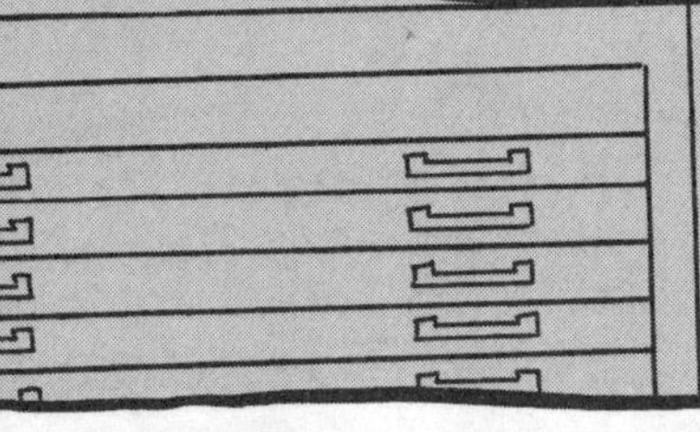

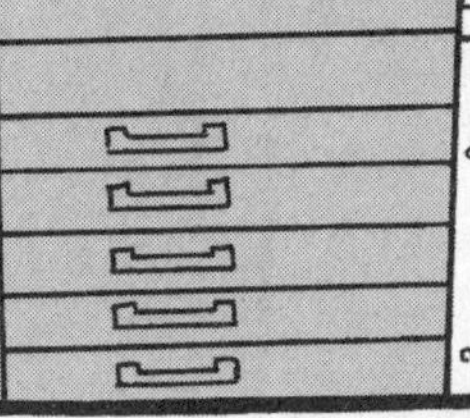

HMMM... I'll have to try that.

Tell your friend I said thanks!

Well, I guess I'll let you get back to your work.

'Bye, Stephen!

'Bye, Jay!

Okay, say hi to the wife for me... See ya Tuesday!

u-Save

u-Save

Dude, that was cruel.

I just wanted to see if he'd tell me she's **dead**.
New!
GO

He never **says** she's dead...
Hell, maybe she's **not**!

Did you see the way he **looked** at you?
$9.49
$8.99

She's dead.
$30.99

Clit ta flit flit flit flit
COO COOO CO

COOO COO COOOO

Hi dad!
Are you ready to go?
UL
The moving van is waiting outside.
Dad?

He's gone.
Yeah, probably happened during the night... body's cold.
Not a bad way to go...

All is forgiven...

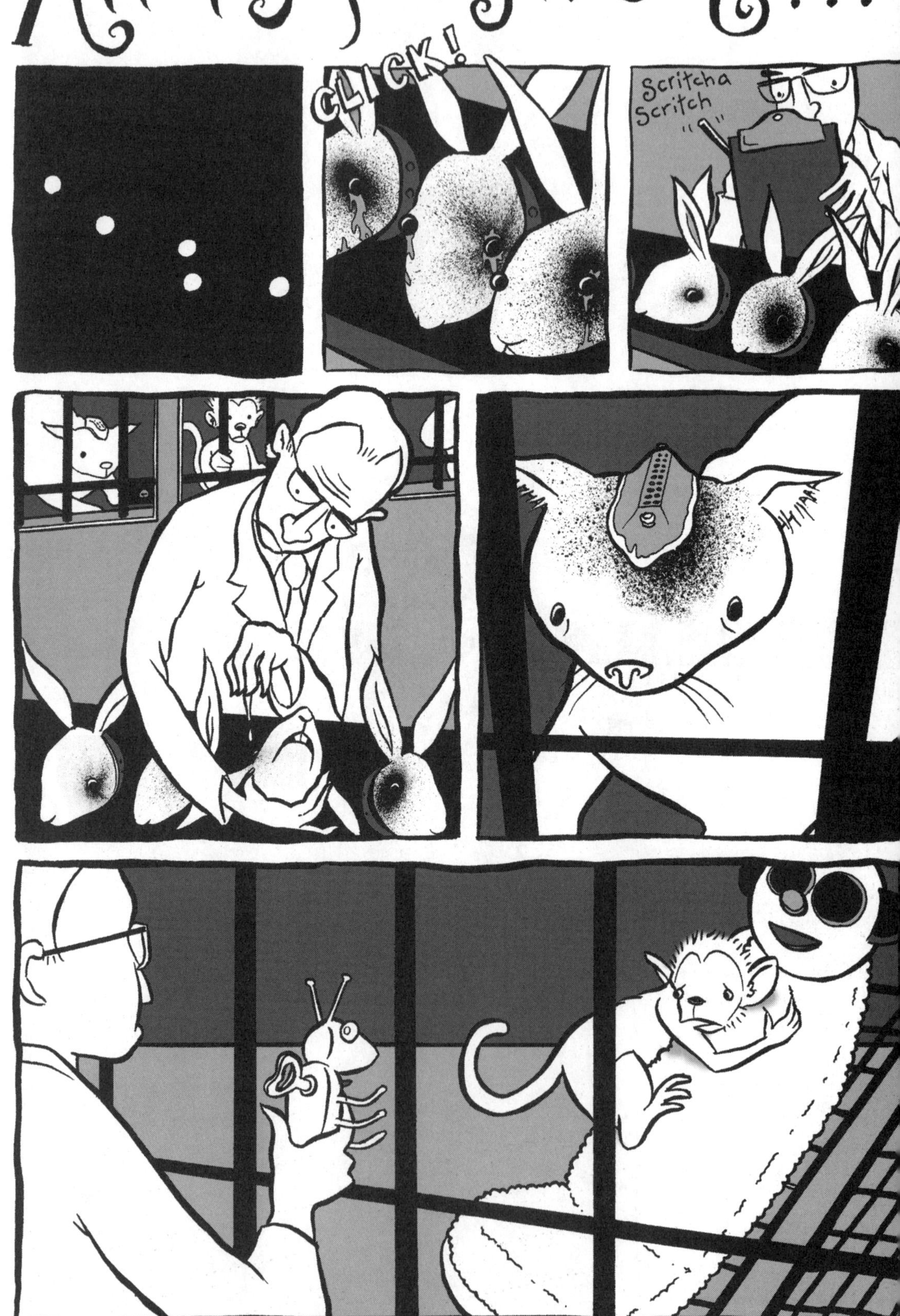
CLICK!
Scritcha Scritch

click
clack

click!

ABORATORY
SLAM!
ZOMBIE
KEYS
dear
this isn't easy
so sorry it
leaving you
don't
ever love
you

click!
lick

LOGGING SANJAY

by J.T. Yost

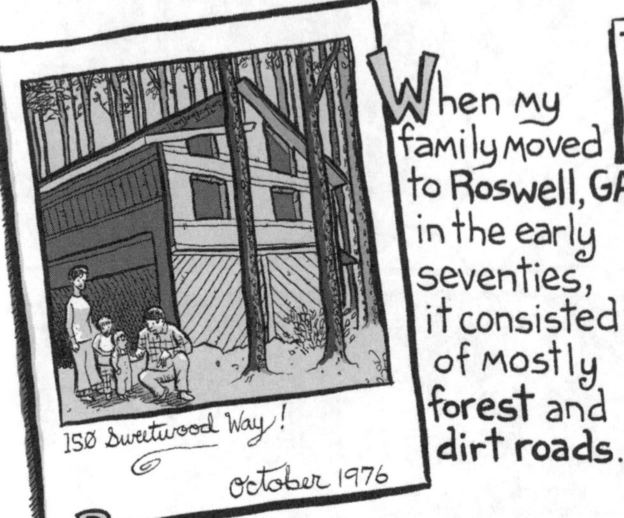

150 Sweetwood Way!
October 1976
When my family moved to **Roswell, GA** in the early seventies, it consisted of mostly **forest** and **dirt roads**.

These days when I visit my parents, I'm **amazed** (and appalled) by the amount of development.

CHUCK Y QUESO
Mexican Pizza Warehouse
yarn barn
the yarn emporium
PETSMORT
the pet mortuary
PETSMORT

Back then, though, it was a kid's dream come true...

...14...15...16...
We spent our days playing in the woods...

Dewey! I caught another **craw-dad**!
Here, put it in the bucket.
...or in the creek.

In high school, my friends and I drove to **Athens** or **Atlanta** to see shows or shop.

...here I go going down down down
my mind is a blank my head is spinning
around and around as i go deep into the
funnel of love it's such a crazy feeling...

Hey Claire! It's that new **Chickasaw Mud Puppies** record!
CHICKASAW MUDD PUPPIES

But when you're **too old** to play in a tree fort, but **not** yet **old enough** to drive into the city, living in a **small town** can become stifling. Boredom can cause you to do some **strange things**...

Sanjay & Matt were my best friends. We always ate lunch together.

One day, Sanjay told us a very bizarre story...
Oh my god! The **weirdest** thing happened this morning!

My dad went to get in his car, and there was a big **log** sitting on top of it.

Maybe it was just a **branch** that fell from a tree.
No, it was a **log**... like you put in a **fireplace**

...Anyway, my mom is convinced **Craig Wagner** put it there.

Why Craig?
She says he's the only guy in our neighborhood **strong** enough to lift the log!

He is kind of brawny.
Sanjay got "**logged**"

The following week I slept over at Matt's house...

HA HA HA HA HA
Ma'am, are you aware of the PENAL CODES in this country?
BAM! BAM BAM
Buddy's shooting cannonballs.* Let's go outside
CHIPS
*Matt's step-father, Buddy, would pound on his bedroom floor when we were being too loud.

Wanna go see if there's any more fireworks in your neighbor's garage?
Nah, I think they suspect I'm taking 'em... Let's see if Sanjay's awake.

His light's off. I guess he's asleep.

We should log him!!
We totally should They'll think it's Wagner again!

Logging Sanjay became a regular activity. We became more creative each time we did it, improvising with what was at hand...

Hey, there's two garbage bags full of grass clippings in the back yard.

We should sprinkle it on the top of the car before we put the log down.
...and fill the mailbox with it!

The reward came the next day as Sanjay recounted his parents' reaction to being logged...

HOLCOM
BRIDGE

Now my mom is **convinced** that it's Craig Wagner because she's seen him mowing his lawn...

I said, "Mom, **everybody** mows their lawns!"

We had two rules: That we would never damage Sanjay's family's car or property, and we would not do anything to scare them. However, after one of our more **involved** sessions, we accidentally broke the second rule ...

Let's tape these cookies to their garage door.

... and my sister's old barbie doll!

We got carried away with a couple of questionable ideas...
uuuh... uuuh! Put it in my mouth-hole!

You get the Playboy channel?
Nah, it's just the sound... the picture is all scrambled.

Ooo look! That's a boob... I think.

Ha ha! We should tape record it and put it on Sanjay's car!

What if we type up a letter demanding payment for our "services"?

Hey! Quit pullin' on the paper!
But it makes it look crappier!

The next day, Sanjay told us what happened...

...so my MOM called the police!
WHAT?!

Yeah, the log Man threatened us.
Threatened you?
diagon Lance

He left a letter saying that we were delinquent on our payment to him for his "services".
That seems more funny than threatening.

Well, he also taped three cookies and a headless doll to our garage window. So, he obviously knows that there are three kids in our family, and that one of us (sanita) is a girl.

Naw, it's probably just a coincidence.

My MOM Made the Police listen to this tape the log Man left. It was porn! She kept looking over at me while the people on the recording are saying real nasty stuff to each other and they're obviously doin' it. You could tell the cop was trying not to laugh.
... Man, it was embarrassing
WORDLY WISE

Sanjay's mom was not a big fan of Matt, so inevitably...

Hey.
My mom sent me to see what kind of cassette tapes and typewriter you've got.
What??

She thinks you're the log man.

Oh, whatever...
I don't have any tapes.

Can I see your typewriter?

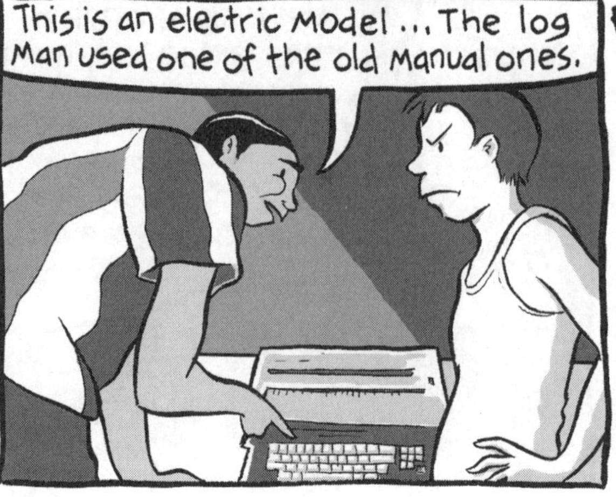
This is an electric model ... The log man used one of the old manual ones.

It was a close call. We stopped logging for a while. Eventually we discovered girls and went on a very very long hiatus from logging Sanjay.

The last time we logged Sanjay, we were old enough to drive a car...

We chopped down a small tree and used the car to drag it all the way over to Sanjay's house.

Both of the windows of his dad's car were open, so we gently slid the tree all the way through the car.

To this day, Sanjay doesn't know who logged him all those years. I've often thought about telling him, so I suppose this is a confessional. Sanjay, if you're reading this, please don't hurt me!!

roadtrip

LE
EADED
jt yost '03

roadtrip

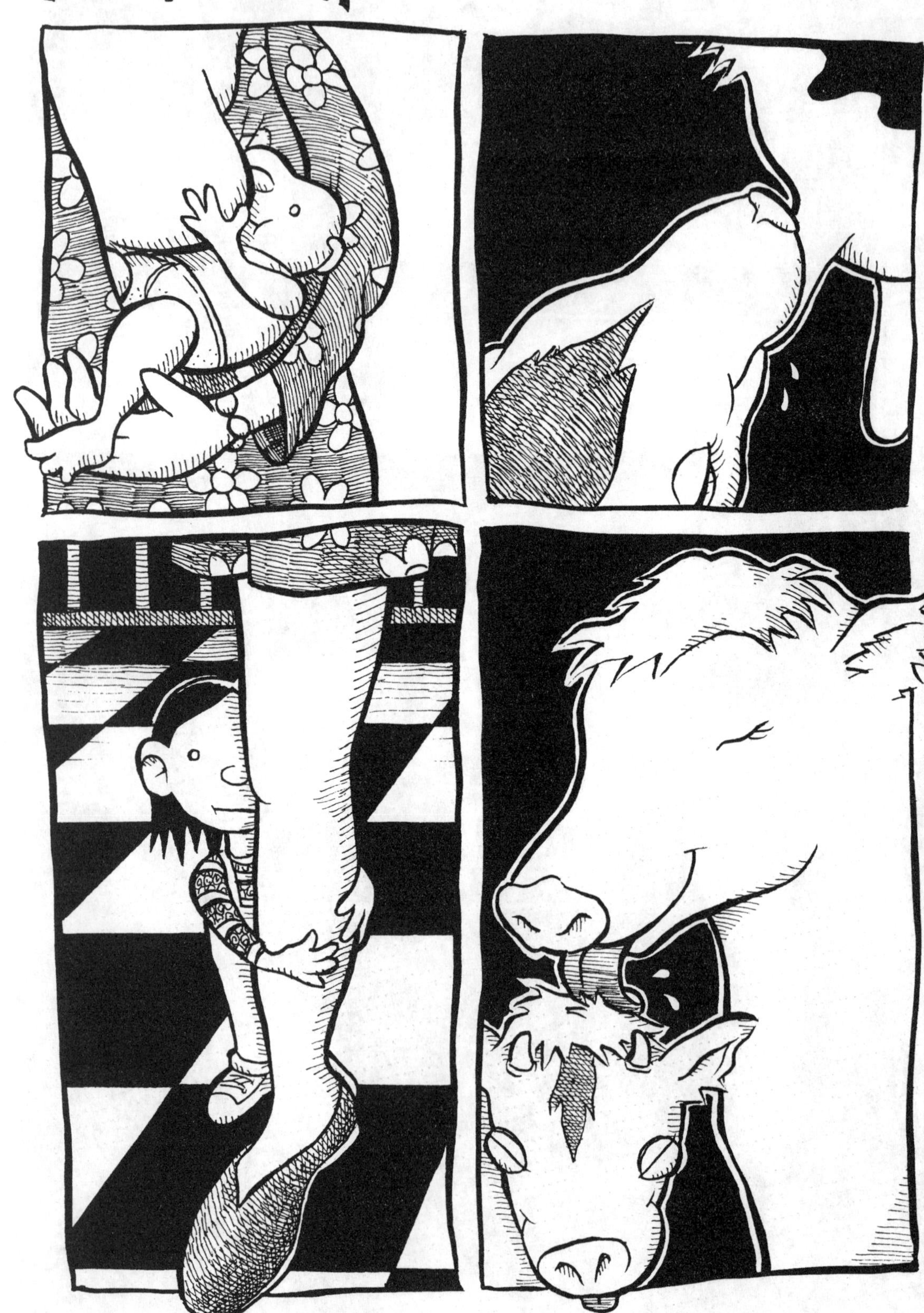

Wee
Rider

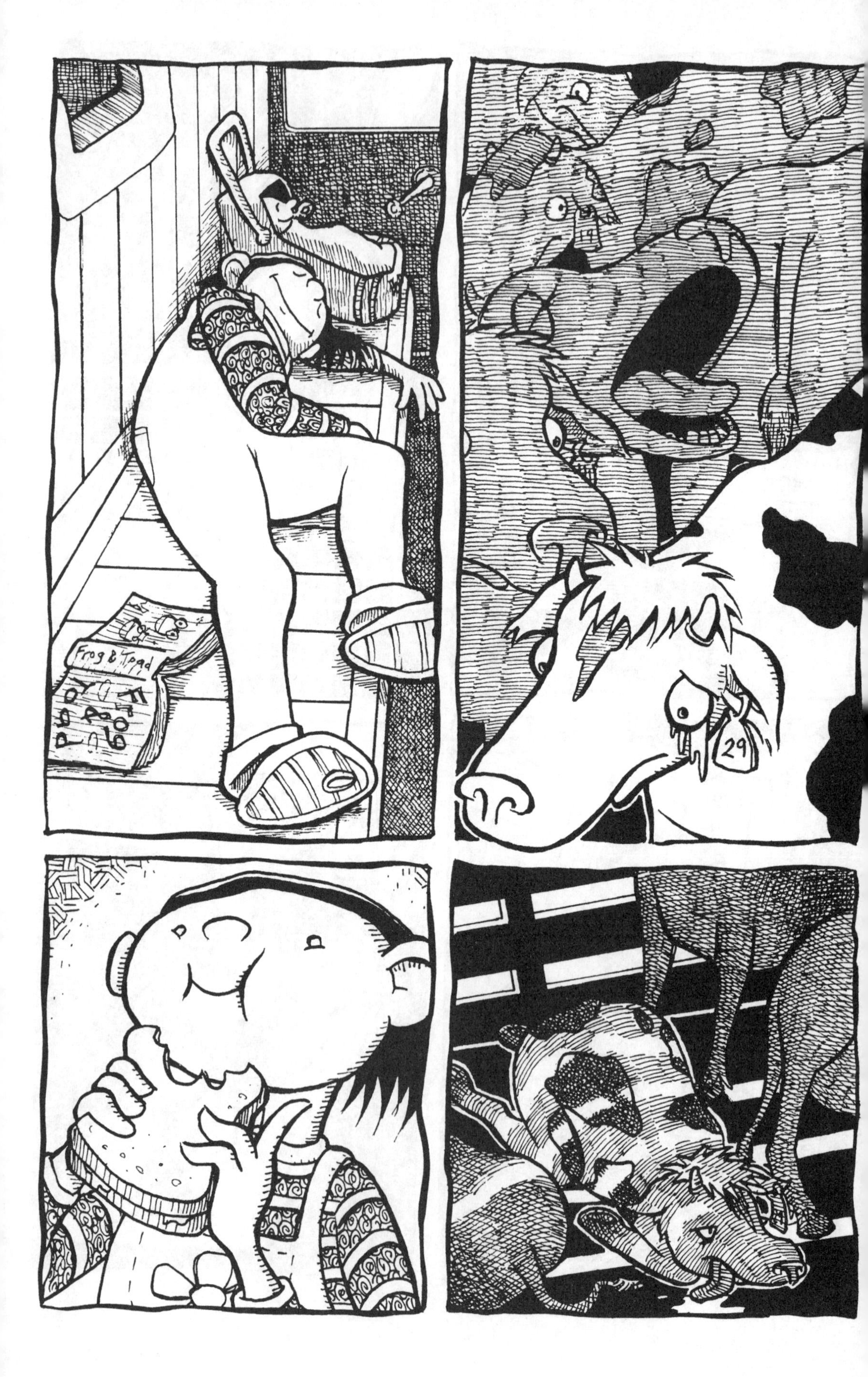
Frog & Toad
29

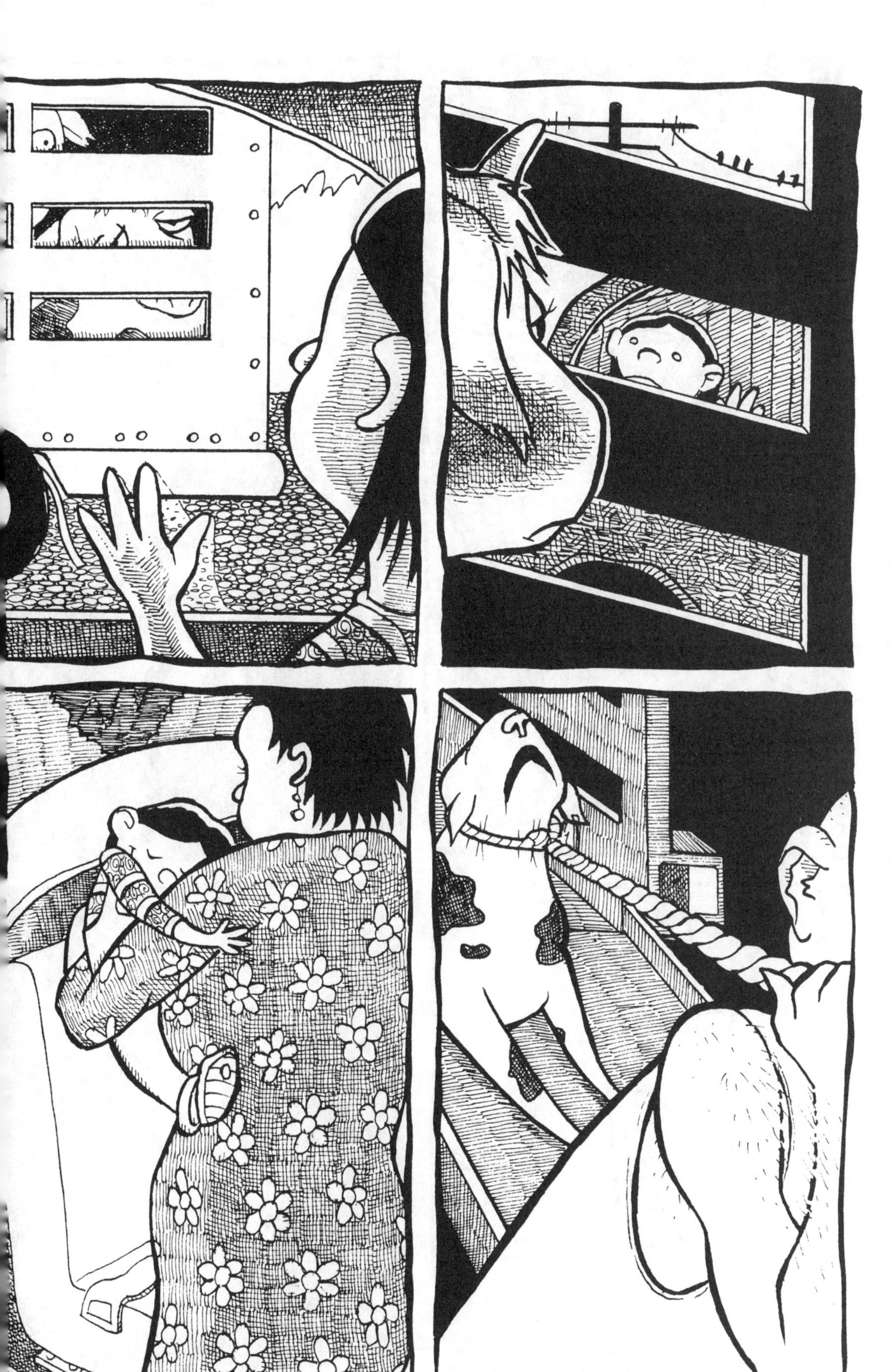

P. P. Penny
Amusement Park
TICKETS

ADMITONE
$17.50
322203

29

ONE HIT WINS

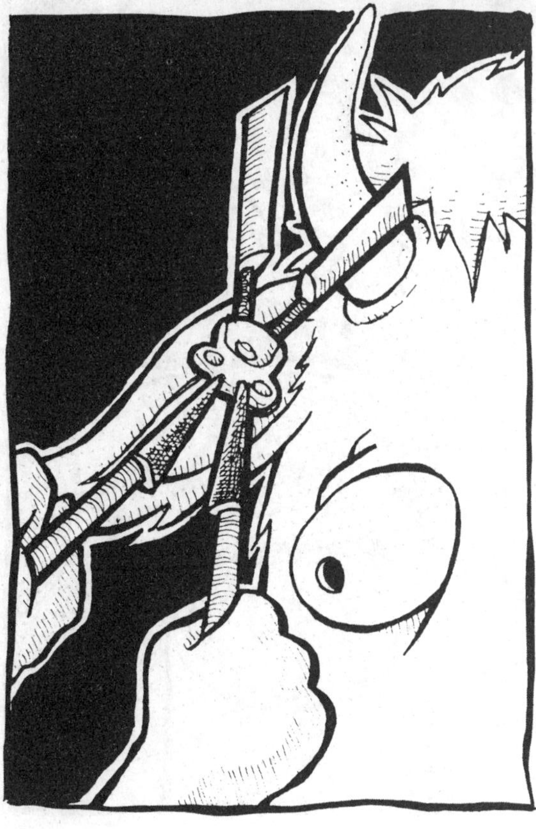

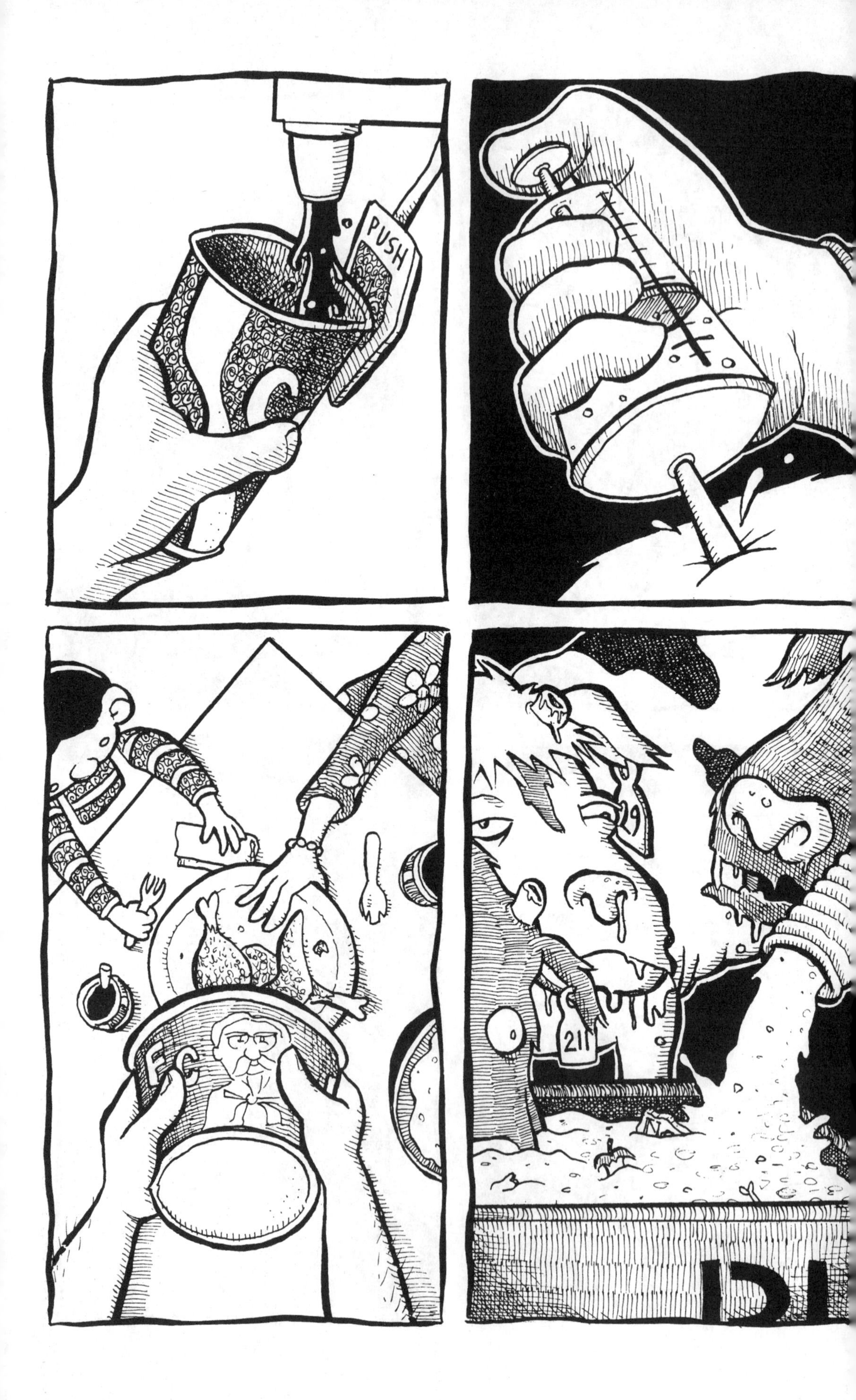
PUSH
29
211

29
AUTO BINGO
AUTO BINGO
COW

FREE TOY!
24pc.

SLAUGHTER
est. 1917

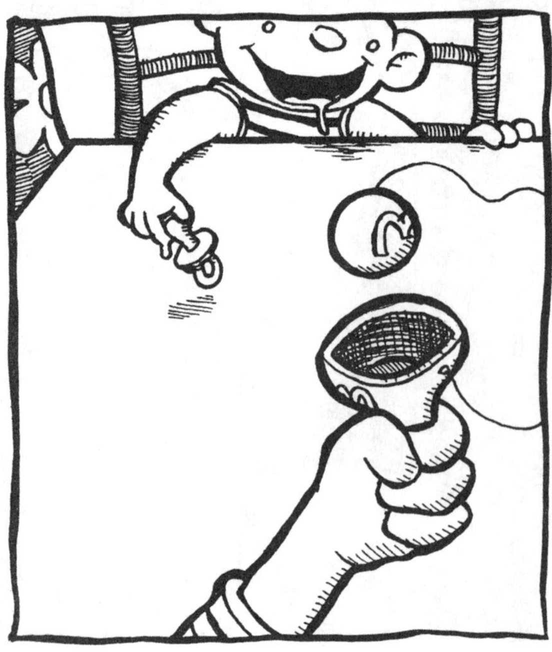

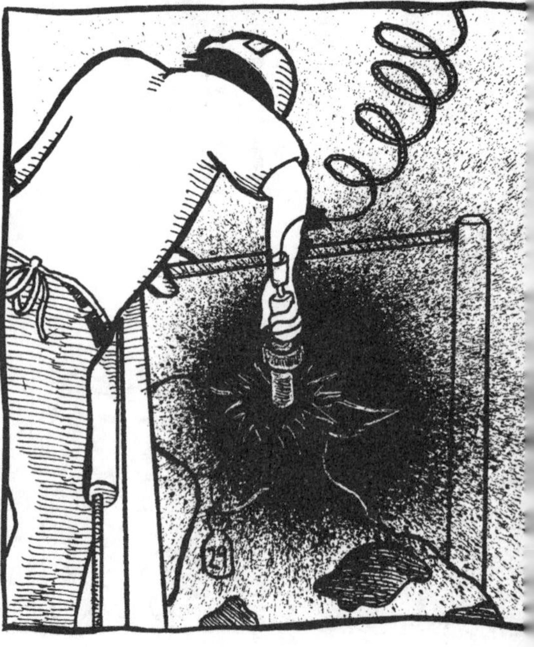

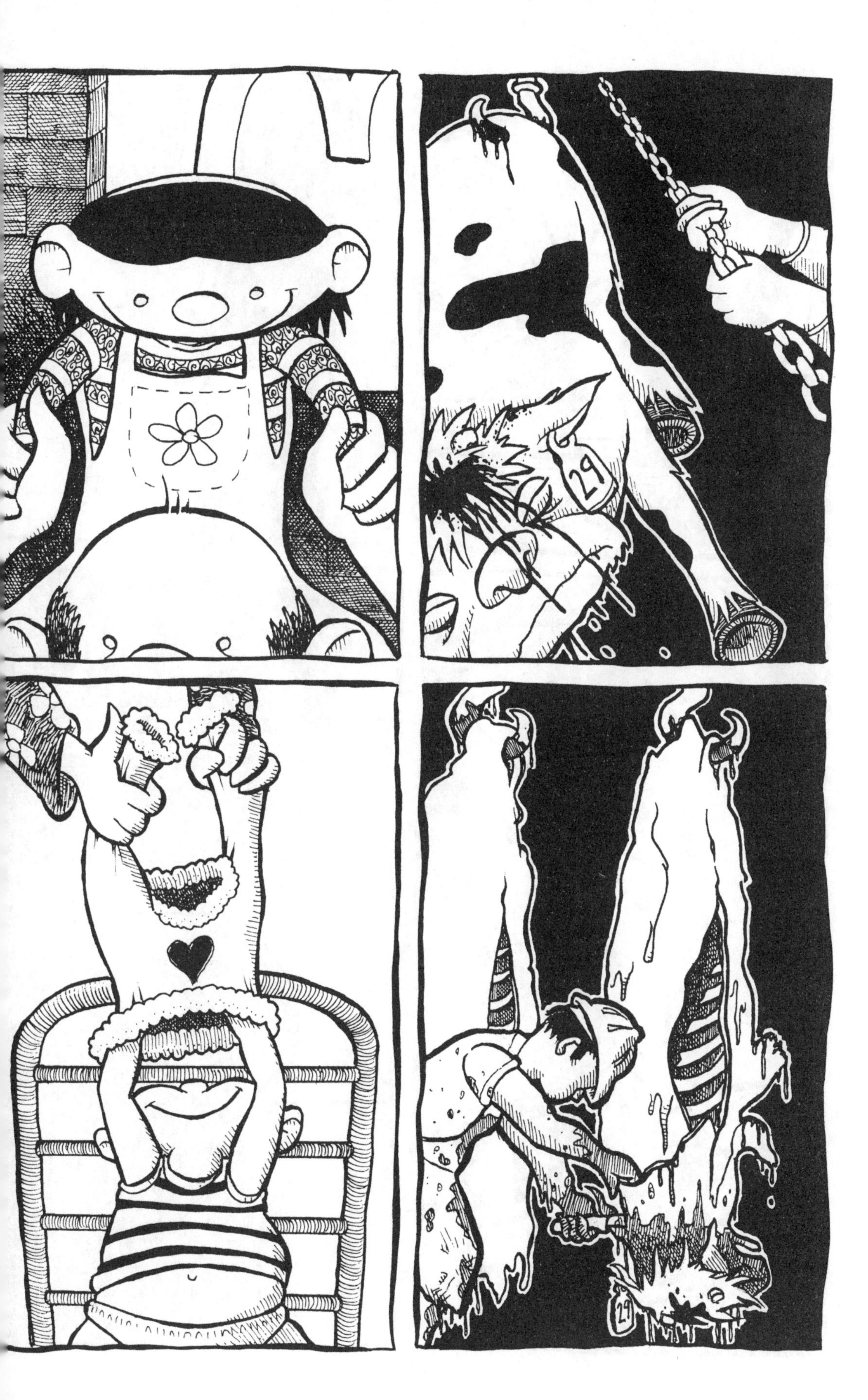
29
29

KNIV
CATSU

BEEF PATTIE
keep frozen
60 pc.

13.30

FREE TOY!

www.jtyost.com

jt 2003

RUNNING AWAY WITH THE CIRCUS

SLAM!

I knew I smelt that DEMON WEED!

This is IT!
You HEAR ME?

This is a GOD FEARIN' house and if you don't FEAR GOD...

Well then yo
DAMN WEL
better
FEAR ME!!

Hey! wake up!

This ain't no place for a boy to sleep... MOVE IT!

CIRCUS

hello?

Sorry kid ...no payin' jobs

You could wo
your way u
if you don
Mind shovel
SHIT!!
HAR
HAR!

2
jt '05

RUNNING AWAY FROM THE CIRCUS

rustle
rustle
thunk
thk
thk
blink
blink
poke
years later
CRASH!
KA-RACK!
jt yost '08

Sincerest thanks to my family & friends (human and otherwise), The Xeric Foundation, and all the cartoonists (and publishers) who were kind enough to share advice & time.